D1536591

Discovering the Cape Cod Shoreline

Gil Newton

To my parents, **John and Hazel Newton**,
for their unconditional love and support.
This book is dedicated to them.

Published by Gilbert Newton
to benefit the Barnstable Land Trust.

gdnewton@comcast.net

ISBN 978-0-9816873-1-5

To purchase a copy of this book, contact:
Barnstable Land Trust
407 North Street, Hyannis, Massachusetts 02601
508-771-2585 • www.BLT.org

Photograph of the author (back cover) by James R. Brown

TABLE OF CONTENTS

ACKNOWLEDGEMENTS

I am very grateful to the following individuals and organizations for their assistance and support:

To **Theresa Mitchell Barbo** for her many years of support to marine studies and conservation, and for her wonderful essay at the beginning of this book.

To **Jaci Barton** for her expertise in reviewing this book and to the **Barnstable Land Trust** for their continuous dedication to conservation.

To **Susan W. Carr** and **Elliott G. Carr** for taking the time to review the section on birds and for all their efforts in helping others understand the Cape's natural history.

To **Chris Dumas** whose outstanding photography once again enhances the written word.

To **Nancy Viall Shoemaker** whose professional guidance helped create this attractive publication.

Nancy Viall Shoemaker

FOREWORD

The Cape Cod shoreline is finally receiving its long overdue ovation.

No longer merely regarded as the sandy thoroughfare between land and salt water, the intertidal zone can now recognized as a unique, dynamic, vibrant and breathing ecosystem, and the reminder and remnant of the receding Laurentian glacier that formed Cape Cod 11,000 years ago.

Species of sea life critical to the marine food chain live out their lives along Cape Cod's intertidal zones, or the shore as the mainstream vernacular calls it.

The shore is comprised, of course, of the sandy beaches and dunes known as microsystems, and even into the sea itself. I count mudflats and marshes as microsystems that can also be part of a larger shore ecosystem, depending on the specific location.

We often can't see every living creature along the shore. From burrowing crabs to lugworms which anchor themselves in the substrate, to weeds floating just beneath the surface of the shore and sponges drifting ashore along the wrack line - these marine species of the intertidal zone find refuge beneath and on the shore. Each creature and the dozens more that call the shore home play a part in their unique environment. Together they create a 'universe' of their own within the embrace of any given Cape Cod shoreline.

We've all taken advantage of the inviting corridor that separates land from sea. Without doubt, many of us take little notice of what's beneath our toes as we look out at the endless horizon. In truth, abundant sea creatures live out their lives within the Cape's numerous intertidal shores. Each tidal zone is as distinct as the beaches that embrace them, from town to town.

In truth, the forests of Cape Cod with their hearty hardwoods have their own magic and few would argue that it's wonderful fun to stroll through the scented and shaded understory of pine, oak, cedar, maple and beech trees, to name a few species here. And who could argue that uplands, stretches of open grassy meadows filled with songbirds, and pastures with their waves of wildflowers, hold their own allure.

But there's something about the shoreline that's inviting and protective at the same time that I wouldn't trade for anything. Without sounding too preachy, the next time you're sea-bound, be aware that the shoreline is a distinct entity in marine biology, as much as the sea is itself distinct, as the dunes are different from an adjoining forest. I personally find the shore soothing and restorative in any season, particularly in deep winter when I can be alone and hear the primal sound of crashing waves.

Gilbert Newton – a scientist and teacher - is a pioneer in the university-grade research, scientific inquiry and public teachings of Cape Cod's intertidal zone. There are few other experts who know as much about the intertidal zone as Gil. While working as Director of the Cape Cod Bay Ocean Sanctuary Program at the Provincetown Center for Coastal Studies – a marine policy and conservation initiative – in 2007, I took two marine biology courses from Gil at Cape Cod Community College and can still remember much of what Gil taught and am amazed at the depth and scope of his knowledge and passion for the subject.

Because of my professional and academic experiences in researching and trying to conserve various marine ecosystems on Cape Cod, I see shorelines through an enlightened lens. The shore intrigues as much as, if not more than, a bay or open ocean.

Gil has a way of explaining the shoreline that is understandable and invites a student to learn about the intertidal zone which can be appreciated for an entire lifetime.

I've come to realize that one cannot appreciate, admire, protect and revel in Cape Cod's full complement of natural resources without also adopting the intertidal zone as a representative fact that the wildlife along the shore provides intrinsic value to our own sense of restoration and recreation.

Theresa Mitchell Barbo
Author and Historian

Yarmouth Port, 2012

The Pleasures of Beachcombing

Since I was a child I have enjoyed the simple pleasures of beach-combing, exploring that part of the natural world that Rachel Carson called 'the edge of the sea." For many this is primarily a summertime activity, though I find exploring the winter beach just as fascinating. Undoubtedly this form of recreation in my childhood inspired me to pursue the study of marine biology. We sometimes take small steps at the beginning of any career. But I still haven't lost the thrill of finding a sea creature, even a very common one, washed up in the wrack line or stranded in a tide pool.

The diversity of life in the sea is amazing, and one can get a sense of such diversity by visiting a sandy or rocky beach, an estuary, or a salt marsh. Each marine habitat has its own characteristic assemblage of organisms determined by specific physical features. Visiting an area at different times of the year, or at high and low tides, can reveal numerous plants and animals that are present under certain conditions.

A large cluster of ribbed mussels (*Modiolus demissus*) can be seen at low tide in the mud flats of a marsh. Clinging tightly to the peat substrate these animals can survive several hours of exposure. When the tide comes in it may be accompanied by large numbers of sea stars (*Asterias spp.*) which pry open the mollusks and feed on the lower rung of mussels. This in turn opens up new space for the colonization of periwinkles (*Littorina littorea*), bry-ozoans, and algae.

The tools for beachcombing are very simple. A small bucket can be used to temporarily contain a specimen for examination. You should return the animal to the place where you found it when finished. I always bring a hand lens with me. It helps with more detailed observations for identification. Some people bring along several field guides to the site, but I'm always afraid of dropping them in the water. Instead, a pocket notebook is handy for brief descriptions and sketches when confronted with an unknown specimen. Of course almost everyone carries a camera or phone for taking photos of anything special.

I never tire of making new discoveries at the shoreline. Occasionally I see something unique or unusual like a large population of salps washing ashore or a group of sea cucumbers left high and dry. Maybe you will witness horseshoe crabs laying their eggs, or an algae bloom of an invasive species, or a hundred hungry mud snails feeding on a dead fish. At any rate there is much to learn at these dynamic systems. The changes are everlasting and will provide a lifetime of excitement and interest.

The Intertidal Zone

Imagine that you are a marine animal fighting for survival and you find yourself in a very difficult environment, one that is periodically exposed and then inundated with water. In addition to this, the substrate is constantly moving and frequently hammered by strong, breaking waves. Oxygen concentrations fluctuate. Salinity levels vary. And the area is constantly surveyed by hungry predators.

Such is the place called the intertidal zone; it is one of the most hostile habitats for marine life. This area between the daily high and low tides is a dynamic system, one in which the sediments are constantly moving. If the beach has a steep profile, it may exhibit very coarse, large materials such as pebbles and rocks. This is often accompanied by strong waves which carry any remaining light sand, making it even more difficult for animals to inhabit. The opposite of this is a quieter and sandier beach with a more uniform profile. Burrowing animals are more likely to be found here.

Of course these sections of a beach can change even more if there are jetties, groins, or seawalls present. Jetties, for example, tend to starve the beach of its sand. Instead of protecting the beach from erosion, jetties

actually accelerate the erosion process. They do this by focusing wave energy on a smaller, more concentrated area. Many coastal communities have lost their beaches because of the numerous jetties built there. An extensive cobble beach exists in Sandwich next to the jetty at the entrance to the Cape Cod Canal.

The animals that are successful inhabitants of the intertidal zone have certain characteristics in common. One is that they are able to burrow deep into the substrate so that they aren't carried away with the next wave. They can also move quite quickly if necessary. At right is one of my favorites, the mole crab (*Emerita talpoida*), a small arthropod with an egg-shaped body and conspicuous antennae that are used to capture small bits of food. There are also

several species of worms that have adapted to life in the intertidal zone. The lugworm (*Arenicola marina*) forms a two-part opening in the substrate and anchors itself by expanding at its base.

Most of the plants and animals seen in this part of the beach have washed up from deeper water. A rocky shoreline provides a more solid substrate for critters to cling or attach to. Such places of attachment and concealment are lacking on a sandy beach.

A Green, a Brown, and a Red
Marine Salad – the Sea Lettuce

Certainly one of the most recognizable seaweeds along the upper region of the shoreline is sea lettuce (*Ulva lactuca*). This green alga consists of large sheets that fold along the edges, much like salad lettuce. It's present year round, but grows abundantly in the summer.

Ulva grows in a variety of habitats that include bays, estuaries, salt marshes, and the intertidal zone. This species has blades that are two cell layers thick and can grow up to three feet in length. There is a small, inconspicuous holdfast, though many specimens are found floating. A similar alga is called *Monostroma oxyspermum*, but it is much thinner with a frond of a single cell layer. Sections of *Ulva* sometimes break apart from the main plant and can continue to grow vegetatively.

The life cycle of *Ulva* is an example of an alternation of generations between a diploid and a haploid stage. The interesting thing is that these two stages are morphologically identical. *Ulva* only lives for a few weeks which helps explain why there are very few epiphytes attached to it. Could the cultivation of *Ulva* be useful in reducing global warming? Sea lettuce has a high rate of photosynthesis and can presumably absorb more atmospheric carbon dioxide. Unfortunately it also decomposes rapidly, thus releasing carbon back into the environment.

However, *Ulva* can be quite useful in other ways. Sea lettuce is adapted to a wide range of salinity and nutrients. It is one of the algae species that grows abundantly in areas of excess nitrogen runoff. Consequently its presence can be an environmental indicator of poor coastal water quality. Nitrogen acts as a fertilizer and can have a serious impact on the health of aquatic ecosystems.

This process of excess nitrogen and the rapid growth of algae such as sea lettuce is called eutrophication. The nitrogen comes from a variety of sources including septic systems, lawn fertilizers, and the atmosphere. When a single species of algae suddenly increases in population, it blocks sunlight to other plants including the ecologically important eelgrass (*Zostera marina*). Bacteria are responsible for the decomposition of the algae. During decomposition bacteria use oxygen, creating low dissolved oxygen concentrations for invertebrates and fish. Crabs, shrimp, mollusks, and small fish can be killed under these conditions. *Ulva* can grow in large sheets in such polluted waters. Observing the presence of abundant sea lettuce can lead to further water testing and remediation efforts.

Ulva's affinity for nitrogen can be put to good use. It could be employed to absorb excess nitrogen near sewer outfalls or fish farms and then applied to gardens to enrich the soil. This natural form of alternative wastewater management will probably not be applied over a wide area, but could be used in smaller, localized situations.

Ulva is also an edible seaweed. Traditionally it is cut up and used in soups and salads. Sea lettuce is high in iron, iodine, and vitamin C. It's about 15% protein and less than 1% fat. In many parts of the world including Scotland and China, sea lettuce is harvested directly from the sea. It should be thoroughly washed to remove any small marine animals. Also keep in mind that it does grow abundantly in areas of high concentrations of nutrient runoff.

The Giant Seaweed

The kelps are a very common group of large seaweeds that grow abundantly on both coastlines. This brown and perennial group of marine algae is important ecologically and economically. The sugar kelp (*Laminaria saccharina*) is the most frequently seen species on southern Cape Cod. A white sugary substance forms on the blade when dried, hence the species name.

Laminaria grows in the deeper subtidal zone attached to rocks with its strong extensive root-like holdfast. The blades are strap-shaped and may grow up to ten feet in length. As it ages, the edges of the blade tend to fold giving it a rippled appearance. Though brown in color, the blades are responsible for photosynthesis, absorbing the necessary ingredients for this important process directly from the water. Though these organisms are non-vascular, they have evolved a series of specialized cells called trumpet hyphae in the stem-like stipe which move sugars and other materials throughout the alga. This stipe is strong, flexible and can grow closer to the water's surface, allowing the blades to maximize photosynthesis. The sugars formed in this process are stored throughout the plant and are consumed by many small animals such as sea urchins. Because of strong waves and currents, these blades sometimes get torn from their holdfast and wash up on nearby beaches.

Like many marine algae, *Laminaria's* life cycle displays an alternation of two morphologically different generations. The large visible plant is the sporophyte which forms clusters of reproductive structures called sporangia along the edges of the blade. These spores are produced in large quantity and released. There they differentiate into either male or female stages called the gametophyte. The male structure is called the antheridium and releases the sperm. The female structure is called the oogonium and releases the eggs. Fertilization occurs and the young zygote grows into the sporophyte stage once again. This life cycle is similar to that of other brown algae including some of the rockweeds.

Kelp beds and forests are valuable habitats to many species of invertebrates and fish. Not only are they grazed upon directly by animals, but they are also a food source when they decompose into bits of organic matter called detritus. In addition many species use the holdfasts of kelp to lay their eggs and hide from predation. Small worms, mollusks and crustaceans can be found living in a kelp bed. Therefore they have an important ecological role in the marine environment as part of this complex food web.

From a human perspective the harvesting of kelp has proven to be a lucrative business. Kelp is widely used in many commercial products. In some parts of the world kelp is eaten directly in soups and salads. In Japan it is used as a soup stock called kombu. An extracted substance called alginate is used as an emulsifier in ice cream, toothpaste and various puddings.

Kelp is also valuable in the garden. Many types of seaweed are an excellent source of compost. They help plants develop healthy root systems while reducing their susceptibility to diseases. Kelp can be purchased as a fertilizer either in a dried or liquid form. This is available as a safe organic alternative to stronger commercial fertilizers that can sometimes damage essential soil microorganisms.

Corallina
A Calcifying Red

As a graduate student I spent many enjoyable hours exploring the subtropical waters of the Florida Keys. There I was able to observe, collect, and study a wide variety of marine algae quite unlike those I was familiar with from Cape Cod. Probably the greatest difference between the two areas was the common occurrence of calcifying algae in the warmer Floridian waters.

These algae have the ability to remove limestone (calcium carbonate) from the water and deposit it on their fronds. Some of the calcifying species are quite common in the Keys including the green *Halimeda*, the brown *Padina*, and the red coralline algae. It's the latter group that interested me because there is a common representative on Cape Cod.

The name of this red alga is *Corallina officinalis*. It's found near jetties and tide pools where it is attached to shells and rocks. I have found it frequently growing on the shells of periwinkle snails. When alive *Corallina* is pink to purple in color, but bleaches white when it dies. Examine it with a hand lens and you can see that the alga is jointed with flexible areas free from lime. This allows it to move back and forth in the waves without breaking. It can grow up to six inches in length and looks like tiny bones under a microscope. There is a small disc-shaped holdfast that attaches to solid objects.

Like other red algae *Corallina's* life cycle includes male and female reproductive structures which release their gametes for fertilization. Following this, specialized spores are released that form a structure called a tetrasporophyte. This results in a reduction division, haploid spores are released, and female and male algae form.

The most obvious question is how do these organisms stay alive when covered in limestone? After all they're photosynthetic so the sunlight needs to reach their tissues. And what is the evolutionary advantage of this ability to calcify? Most scientists believe that enough light penetrates this armored layer to allow photosynthesis to take place. And possibly the limestone coating discourages animals from grazing on their soft tissues, though sea urchins, which need the lime for their shells, may consume the coralline algae.

Without coral reefs on the Cape, *Corallina* stands out as an unusual member of the diverse algae in this region. It is easily recognized on the shore and can be quite abundant in some areas. At one point in history it was used to remove intestinal worms in humans. Today it's the lone representative in the northeast of a much larger and significant group of algae that dominate the tropics.

The larger number of calcifying algae in the tropics is due to the fact that limestone is easier to remove in warmer waters because it goes into solution more readily in colder water. In spite of this disadvantage *Corallina* is quite successful in its calcification and is very common in the northeast. Dried specimens can be stored in jars for many years.

Discovering the Cape Cod Shoreline

Gil Newton

The Values of Rockweed

An interesting example of a community of interacting plants and animals occurs along the banks of a salt marsh. At low tide one can observe a distinct zone in which the cordgrass (*Spartina alterniflora*) occupies the upper portion. Its extensive root system can be seen in the mud, along with a large ribbed mussel (*Modiolus demissus*) population. These animals are attached to the peat and to each other by strong byssal threads. The mussels are filter-feeders and use their siphons to strain water for small particles of food.

Present also is a healthy population of rockweed (*Fucus vesiculosus*) which grows in the muddy banks and often covers the clumps of mussels. This alga is common on jetties, pilings, and other hard surfaces. The general characteristics of rockweed are easy to identify. The brown, forked branches have pairs of small air bladders along the midrib of the frond which help the alga float in the water. The alga is attached to a hard surface by a structure called a holdfast. Sometimes the tips are swollen with small bumps which contain the reproductive conceptacles. The  male conceptacles release motile sperm cells in the water when the tide comes in. The female conceptacles release the egg cells that are carried by water current. A single sperm cell fertilizes an egg cell and the resulting zygote settles down on a solid surface. It then grows into a new rockweed plant.

Ecologically, rockweed has many functions. It forms a kind of canopy protecting the mussels, barnacles, and other life forms during low tide. Some invertebrates and small fish graze on the rockweed, while other species, such as the periwinkles, scrape the microscopic diatoms and bacteria from the fronds. Like the cordgrass, the rockweed becomes food for other animals in deeper water. When the plants die, they decompose and break up into small organic bits of food called detritus. This gets swept up by the tides and currents, and transported to other areas as a source of nutrition.

Though rockweed is brown due to the presence of the pigment fucoxanthin, it can photosynthesize and is a primary producer in the salt marsh. Therefore, it also releases oxygen and absorbs carbon dioxide. Physically it helps prevent erosion along the banks by reducing the impact of wave energy. Examine a small piece of rockweed with a hand lens and you may see the young larval stages of many animals, as well as tiny tube worms and encrusting bryozoans.

The Clambake Alga

One of the largest and most important seaweeds is *Ascophyllum nodosum*, commonly called knotted wrack. *Ascophyllum* is one of the largest rockweeds on the east coast and can grow up to three feet long. The fronds are characterized by several large and single air bladders (pneumatocysts), but have no distinct midrib like in *Fucus*. Though *Ascophyllum* is a brown alga (Phaeophyta), it can have an olive greenish tinge.

The knotted wrack is attached to a hard substrate, such as a rock jetty, by means of a small holdfast. This alga usually grows from the mid to lower levels of the intertidal zone. As with other rockweeds this alga releases the gametes or reproductive cells from their swollen receptacles at the tips. The swelling occurs at low tide and the gametes are released when the tide comes in. Following fertilization the young alga settles to the substrate for attachment and subsequent growth.

The pneumatocysts give the alga buoyancy during high tide. This ability to float exposes a greater surface area for the fronds to increase photosynthesis. In this process the alga, like true plants, converts water and carbon dioxide to oxygen and sugars. Though the alga's brown color is due to the pigment fucoxanthin, it also contains chlorophyll needed for photosynthesis. These pneumatocysts are the largest among the rockweeds.

Ascophyllum is an important seaweed for other forms of marine life. Many small organisms such as snails, sand hoppers, and crabs find shelter under its fronds. This provides them with protection from predators and desiccation at low tides on warm days. Even small lobsters and fish find shelter here. Periwinkle snails will graze on the microscopic diatoms attached to the rockweed. There is a small red alga, *Polysiphonia lanosa*, which is attached to the *Ascophyllum*. This is in spite of the fact that *Ascophyllum* releases a chemical to prevent herbivores from grazing on it.

Ascophyllum nodosum is also economically important. Like other brown algae it produces a substance called algin which is used in a variety of commercial products as an emulsifier or thickener. From puddings to ice cream, the alginates are an important additive to food products. But it doesn't stop there. Medicines, cosmetics, and even the paper industry use this substance.

Traditionally knotted wrack is an excellent seaweed for clambakes. A pile of *Ascophyllum* contains enough moisture to provide the steam in cooking clams and vegetables. This ability to retain moisture also makes it a suitable packing material for lobsters and other seafood. Unfortunately, some areas have been stripped of *Ascophyllum* for this purpose. Care must be exercised to conserve a resource that will replenish itself if not over-harvested.

Discovering the Cape Cod Shoreline

Plants of the Dunes

A stable sand dune is one characterized by a diversity of vegetation. The most conspicuous and probably the most important species is beach grass (*Ammophila breviligulata*). This native grass grows up to three feet tall. The leaves form clumps that trap blowing sand, holding the small particles in place. This prevents erosion and the movement of dunes onto roads. The plants also spread with underground rhizomes that send up shoots, adding to the dune's stability.

There are several other plants that are found on a sand dune. A common shrub is the salt spray rose (*Rosa rugosa*). Though this is an introduced species, its red fruits, called rose hips, are a food source for several animals. In addition, the salt spray rose also helps control erosion and is quite attractive with its large white, pink, or red flowers. The rose hips have been used as a vitamin-rich jelly.

Another dune shrub that has had a history of commercial use is bayberry (*Myrica pensylvanica*). The slightly round leaves have small teeth on the tips. The fruits are ball-shaped and gray. They appear waxy to the touch, a feature that helps protect the plant from dehydration. These berries have been used to make aromatic soaps and candles.

A smaller branched shrub with scale-like leaves often grows in patchy mounds on a sand dune. This is called poverty grass or beach heather (*Hudsonia tomentosa*) and is one of the few evergreen plants in this habitat. The small yellow flowers can  be seen in the summer. The plant has a grayish tinge to it, and sometimes grows in very dense patches.

There are two common dune plants which belong to the genus *Artemisia*. At left is dusty miller (*A. stelleriana*) which has distinct grayish-green leaves covered with small hairs that function to protect the plant from dehydration. This plant also puts out a long spike of yellow flowers in mid to late summer. However, it is the lobed foliage that makes it an ideal addition to gardens. Its relative is wormwood (*A. caudata*) which has pinnate leaves that grow close to the substrate. Less conspicuous than dusty miller, wormwood also produces small yellow flowers in the summer.

Growing at the base of the dunes is a colorful legume called the beach pea (*Lathyrus japonicus*). This plant lies low on the ground and exhibits bright purple flowers in the summer which are followed by the typical fruits of a pea plant. This is another plant that is adapted to the dry, sandy soil. The small leaves spread out at the dune's edge.

Discovering the Cape Cod Shoreline

In many areas in the northeast goldenrod is one of the most visible and showiest wildflowers. However, there is a species that has adapted to the harsh dune environment, namely seaside goldenrod (*Solidago sempervirens*). This plant can grow several feet high and produces bright yellow flowers in late summer to early fall. The leaves are thick and up to a foot in length which helps retain water. The flowers are often visited by large numbers of insects that assist in pollination.

We end our dune tour with one of my favorites, the hardy beach plum (*Prunus maritima*). Known for its delicious fruits which are made into jams and jellies, beach plum also produces showy white flowers in late spring. The dark purple fruits appear later in the summer. The leaves on this shrub are toothed and the plant, like so many others in this habitat, is good for erosion control.

NVS

The Most Important Plant

If I was asked to select a single plant species that has had a major environmental influence on Cape Cod, I would choose *Spartina alterniflora*, also called cordgrass. This species is a perennial plant that grows up to eight feet tall and is one of the more conspicuous vascular plants in the marsh. Cordgrass is found along the lower part of the salt marsh in the daily tide zone.

When you examine a population of cordgrass growing along the edge of the marsh, you might wonder how it can possibly survive in such a hostile environment. After all, any plant surrounded by a salty system will lose water to the environment. However, this species has a unique way of dealing with that problem. In order to survive the exposure to sea water, cordgrass removes salt through its leaves. Rub your fingers along one of its blades and you can feel the tiny salt crystals.

The plant has also evolved another unique adaptation to the salt marsh. The substrate is an anaerobic environment which would normally be fatal to any other plant. However, cordgrass has specialized cells in the leaves for moving oxygen to the roots, thus providing their own source of needed oxygen.

NVS

Discovering the Cape Cod Shoreline

21

Another interesting ecological feature of this plant is that it creates a protective habitat for both rockweed and ribbed mussels. The rockweed acts as a canopy over the mussels while the cordgrass stabilizes the land and banks for the attachment of the seaweed. This form of zonation is particularly visible at low tide.

When cordgrass dies and decomposes, it forms large mats of decaying vegetation called detritus. Some of these mats are transported into the bay where they are consumed by numerous microorganisms and tiny animals. This detritus represents an important organic food source. It ultimately supports invertebrates and fish, either through direct grazing or indirectly as an energy source through the food web.

A portion of the mat may remain at the high tide mark or wash into tiny pools, or pannes, in the marsh. There it provides additional nutrients and shelter for small living things, as well as enrichment of the sediments as it decomposes.

Sometimes large chunks of peat break away from the banks of a marsh. These small islands are called hummocks and may have a population of cordgrass already attached. If positioned correctly in one of the creeks, they can get established with the grass continuing to trap additional sediments. This is one way that the marsh can grow and expand.

Ironically, this important species in Massachusetts is considered a pest in other parts of the country such as Washington and California. It has become invasive in parts of those states and has out-competed several native species. But here it is at the top of my list for significant plants along the coastline.

The Primitive Sponges

When you go into a store to purchase a package of sponges, chances are they are made of cellulose. These commercially produced sponges have replaced the real sponges that were once collected by divers. These real sponges are very primitive animals in the phylum Porifera which means "pore-bearing." Though considered primitive by most zoologists, there are about 10,000 different species living today.

A sponge is a simple animal. It has no organs or organ systems. There are no digestive, excretory, nervous, or muscular systems. Instead, a typical sponge has a body wall with three layers. The first is the epidermis or outside layer that contains many pores. Internal to this layer is a matrix of skeletal-like particles known as spicules, though there are exceptions. Finally there is an inner layer composed of specialized cells called choanocytes or collar cells which beat the water, setting up small currents that flow into the sponge through the pores. Small food particles get trapped and are digested. They are also considered filter-feeders because of this method of obtaining nutrition.

There are three basic types of sponges. The first and simplest is the asconoid sponge. These animals are characterized by a central cavity with a single opening to the outside known as an osculum. They are usually very small sponges, just a few centimeters high. The second type is the syconoid sponge. These sponges demonstrate an increasing amount of folding, therefore increasing the surface area. This leads to improved feeding efficiency. Finally, there are the leuconoid sponges which are the largest and most common. There is a much greater amount of body wall folding in leuconoid sponges.

Sponges may reproduce asexually and sexually. In asexual reproduction a sponge can reproduce by budding off a new segment, by regenerating a whole sponge from small fragments, or by producing small cyst-like gemmules which are highly resistant to environmental stress conditions. The regeneration process is fascinating. In some species a small piece of a sponge can be ground up and will reassemble into a new sponge. In sexual reproduction most sponges are hermaphroditic, that is they contain both male and female reproductive structures. Other sponges have separate sexes.

Sponges are mostly marine, yet there are several freshwater species. Several cold-water sponges can be found washed up on Cape Cod beaches, and on pilings, shells, and wharves. Oysters and quahogs, as shown at right, are often riddled with holes from the boring sponge (*Cliona celata*).

Deadman's fingers (*Haliclona occulata*) can be found on the beach after a storm. There are several less conspicuous, but common, species of sponges in this area. It may be difficult to imagine sponges as animals, but they are highly successful in evolution and very well adapted to their environment.

Marine Mollusks on Cape Cod

From a sandy beach to a salt marsh, the remains of one of the largest invertebrate groups can be found. The Mollusca is only second to the insects in number of species. The two main groups are the bivalves (clams) and the gastropods (snails). Both groups have a mantle which forms the outside shell made of calcium carbonate. The shell grows larger as the animal increases in size. The body of the animal is soft and unsegmented.

The clam shell consists of two halves or valves which are attached by a hinge. These animals are filter feeders taking in water through a siphon and trapping and selecting small food particles. The snails have a single shell and feed by scraping their food with a radula. Some snails are herbivores while others are carnivores.

There are two common species of mussels. The blue mussel (*Mytilus edulis*) can be found on intertidal rocks and jetties. Bluish-black in color, this animal grows to over three inches. It is attached to its substrate with strong byssal threads. This is the edible species and it is consumed by many predators ranging from sea stars to eider ducks.

The ribbed mussel (*Modiolus demissus*) is more likely found on the banks of salt marshes. This clam has shells with ridges or ribs along the length, hence its name. Both species of mussels are filter-feeders, using their siphons to strain water for bits of organic material such as microscopic algae. They are often covered by a canopy of rockweed *(Fucus vesiculosus)* which provides the animals with protection from predators and desiccation at low tide.

Soft-shelled clams (*Mya arenaria*) have a chalky white shell and are three to six inches long. These animals are commercially important and are often called steamers. They live in muddy intertidal areas and are characterized by a strong foot that anchors the animal and by a large siphon for filtering food.

Razor clams (*Ensis directus*) are also found in mudflats. These mollusks burrow under the surface, but they use their strong foot to dig very quickly into the substrate. The shell is about five times longer than it is wide and is brown along the edges.

Another clam with a chalky white shell is one of the largest bivalves called the surf clam (*Spisula solidissima*). This shell can be up to eight inches in length. The animal is found in deeper water down to one hundred feet. It often washes up on beaches after a major storm.

Another subtidal species that is economically important is the bay scallop (*Aequipecten irradians*). These bivalves do not burrow in the sand but move by snapping their two shells together. They are found in eelgrass habitats and grow up to three inches long.

A very productive and commercially important bivalve is the oyster (*Crassostrea virginica*). An oyster can spawn several times a summer and in the process release millions of eggs. After fertilization the young larvae, known as spat, settle on a hard substrate where they remain for the rest of their lives. Oysters are often found in large clumps next to others because the old shells in

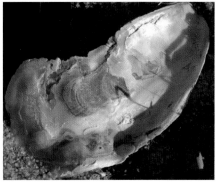

an oyster bed are suitable places to attach. There are many predators of oysters including the small, but highly efficient oyster drill (*Urosalopinx cinera*) which can cut a small hole in the oyster and feed on the animal.

Moon snails (*Polinices duplicatus*) are also carnivorous and do a great deal of damage to a clam or oyster bed. They have a large foot for burying in the sand where they also leave conspicuous trails that can be seen at low tide. Sometimes you can find their egg masses in a circular sandy structure called a sand collar.

There are several common gastropods or snails found on Cape beaches. The largest is the channeled whelk (*Busycon canaliculatum*) which can grow as big as seven to nine inches. This is a carnivorous animal and feeds on various bivalves by using its shell to break open the clams for

feeding. You can often find their long brown egg capsules in which each parchment has over a dozen young whelks. A similar species is the knobbed whelk (*Busycon carica*) which has the bumps or knobs on the outer shell.

The slipper snail or boat snail (*Crepidula fornicata*) is very common in this area, particularly along sandy beaches. Sometimes large numbers of slipper snail shells wash up. They also can be found in large heaps attached to each other. The larger ones on top are female whereas the smaller animals underneath are males. The shell is identified by an indentation or platform along its opening.

In terms of numbers the slipper snail's rival is the periwinkle (*Littorina littorea*). These small snails grow up to one and a half inches long. They are found in the intertidal zone as well as on jetties and groins. They are characterized by a radula for grazing on small plankton and algae, and by a strong foot for moving. They can be seen leaving long tracts in the sand.

Coastal Crabs

For those who like to explore marshes, bays, and estuaries with a hand net or small seine, the catch often includes representatives of the crustacean group. Several species of marine crabs are commonly found on Cape Cod in its shallow waters. The "shell" of the crab is called a carapace and this exoskeleton is composed of a material called chitin. There are three major parts to a crab: the head, thorax, and abdomen. These animals also have jointed appendages and use gills for breathing. They grow through a process called molting in which the carapace splits open and the animal emerges.

Crabs are not difficult to identify. One of the most commercially important species is the blue crab (*Callinectes sapidus*). An aggressive species, this animal is bright blue and has nine teeth along both sides of its shell. The hind legs are shaped like a paddle and it is a very fast swimmer.

Green crabs (*Carcinus maenus*) are quite abundant under small rocks in the inter-tidal zone. This animal was introduced from Europe but has become one of the most commonly seen crabs on the Cape's shoreline. One of the reasons it has been so successful is its tolerance for changes in salinity. The green crab feeds mainly on worms and clams.

Another common crab on Cape Cod is found in estuaries and bays, but look carefully because this animal is an expert at camouflage. The spider crab (*Libinia emarginata*) has a brown carapace with long, spindly legs. It has the ability to stick small shells and algae on its  carapace. Unlike the blue crab, this animal is harmless and can be picked up without any difficulty.

 To examine one of the most interesting coastal crabs, go to a salt marsh in the summer at low tide. Scurrying in the mud will be hundreds of fiddler crabs (*Uca pugnax*) which can be easily caught. Their burrows are scattered throughout the banks and extend about three feet deep. The males are distinct from the females in  that they have a large claw that is used for courtship and defense. These animals are ecologically important to the salt marsh. They are a food source for many animals and they aerate and fertilize the marsh sediments.

You might collect a crab that is in the process of molting. If it's just about to emerge from its shell, it's called a peeler. If it has recently grown from its old shell it will still be soft. It takes a little bit of time for the carapace to harden. Some animals may also appear to be at different stages of regeneration as they slowly replace lost limbs or claws.

The Primitive Horseshoe Crab

There is a remarkable primitive animal that lives in the Cape's shallow waters. It has survived the reign of the dinosaurs and continues today, 350 million years after it evolved. Its blue blood contains a substance capable of detecting bacterial endotoxins. The shell contains a material that can increase the healing of wounds. It looks formidable but is harmless to humans. Indeed it has probably saved many human lives. It is, of course, the horseshoe crab (*Limulus polyphemus*), a common inhabitant of the Atlantic coast.

Horseshoe crabs are not true crabs. Instead they are more closely related to spiders. That is easy to believe when one examines its underside morphology. There are five pairs of legs that enable the animal to crawl along the substrate where it feeds on worms and mollusks. There is a pair of small pincers called chelicerae which assists the animal in feeding. A set of book gills is used for breathing and swimming.

The shell or carapace of the animal is actually an exoskeleton. As the animal grows larger it needs to molt. It does this by splitting the carapace and emerging head first. True crabs molt from the back. It's not unusual to find large numbers of recently molted shells on the Cape's beaches in late summer. It takes about twelve hours for the soft new shell to harden.

A female horseshoe crab will lay thousands of eggs during the spring full moon high tides. These are then fertilized by the smaller male and soon hatch out. In places such as Delaware Bay, horseshoe crabs are an important food source for thousands of migratory birds such as red knots and sanderlings. Without this essential food source many birds would not survive the long migration to northern grounds.

Recently horseshoe crab numbers along the east coast have declined. Many causes are suspect including coastal pollution, the lysate industry which uses the animal's blood, and even the taking of crabs for lobster traps. Several states have imposed restrictions on their harvesting; some areas have been set aside to conserve horseshoe crab populations. Close monitoring and research is necessary to protect this important species. It would be a shame to lose an animal that has survived for millions of years.

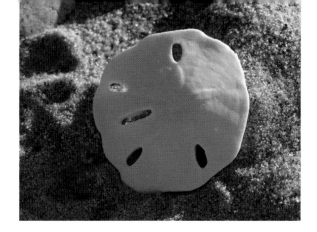

The Echinoderms

On a recent trip to the Crocker Neck Salt Marsh in Cotuit, my students discovered an unusual looking animal in the wrack line. It turned out to be a hairy sea cucumber (*Sclerodactyla briareus*). This species, seen at right, belongs to the group echinoderms which also includes sea stars and sand dollars.

These interesting animals are slow moving critters which live on or near the ocean substrate. They have a thick skin covered with small tube feet that enable them to crawl slowly on the ocean floor. They feed on small bits of food such as algae and are dark in color. If disturbed these animals exhibit a unique method of protection. They will discharge some of their internal organs. Like other echinoderms they can quickly regenerate these lost structures.

As a young beachcomber one of my favorite animals along the sandy shore was the sand dollar (*Echinarachnius parma*) with its characteristic star-shaped pattern on its circular shell. These attractive echinoderms are purple when alive, but their dead white shells or tests (shown above) wash ashore after a storm. These animals move very slowly, feeding on microscopic algae and animals. They, in turn, are a food source for groundfish such as flounder.

The Echinodermata is a unique group of animals found exclusively in the marine environment. They all possess an endo-skeleton and move with tube feet that grip the surface like tiny suction cups. The sea stars are characterized by an elaborate series of internal canals for the movement of water called a water vascular system. Another interesting feature of this group is that they are an important part of the zoo-plankton, though their larval stages don't resemble the adults at all.

Sea urchins belong to this group also and have their own set of unique features. For example, these animals like to graze mainly on large algae, such as kelp, and use a chewing structure called Aristotle's lantern. Even though the purple (*Arbacia punctulata*) and green (*Strongylocentrotus droebachiensis*) urchin species on Cape Cod are covered with spines, they are harmless to people. Sometimes you find their spineless shells on the beach after they die.

Of course the sea stars or starfish (*Asterias vulgaris*) are the most frequently seen, usually in tide pools or protected in the crevices of rock jetties. Sea stars love to feed on bivalve mollusks, particularly mussels. Their arms attach to the mussel, pry it open, and slide their stomach inside the clam to digest it. Occasionally you will find a sea star that is missing one of its five arms or you will notice one with a stubby arm. These animals have a strong ability to regenerate any lost limbs. It may take up to a year, but the animal has no problem surviving as it regenerates.

In spite of their evolutionary longevity and strong adaptive features, echinoderms are also adversely impacted by environmental contamination. Global warming has resulted in the acidification of seawater, reducing the calcification process essential to these animals. And any changes in their benthic habitats from bottom trawling to oil spills can also reduce their populations.

Birds Along the Shore

Many different bird species can be observed along the Cape's shoreline throughout the year. Some birds forage along the intertidal zone while others swim and feed in the open water. Some species congregate close to the shore and can be seen in marshes and estuaries.

Of course the most visible are the "seagulls" which are actually several different species of gulls. The most common is the herring gull (*Larus argentatus*), an abundant scavenger that feeds on mollusks, crabs, and all the food garbage left by people. The herring gull can grow over two feet tall and has black tips on the wings. This animal is overpopulated in many areas and is very competitive with other species, including many endangered ones. A similar species, the ring-billed gull (*Larus delawarensis*) has a conspicuous black ring around its yellow bill.

The great black-backed gull (*Larus marinus*) is not as common. It can grow a few inches larger than the herring gull and can be identified by its dark back, hence its common name.

Elliott G. Carr

Common terns (*Sterna hirundo*) are frequently seen near the gulls They can be identified by their forked tails, black caps, and orange bill. These animals are often seen diving in the water for fish. They are very protective of their nesting sites and will respond noisily to any intruders.

The coastal waters of the Cape are teeming with several species of ducks. Mallard ducks (*Anas platyrhynchos*) are often seen in pairs in the pannes of a salt marsh. The male is brightly colored and has a characteristic green head, whereas the female is brown.

The American black duck (*Anas rubripes*) grows up to two feet long and can be seen year round in the marshes.

E G Carr

The common eider (*Somateria mollissima*), above, is seen even in the winter. The male eider has a distinct white back, but is black underneath. The females are brown.

Discovering the Cape Cod Shoreline

Another sea bird often seen with the eiders are buffle-heads (*Bucephala albeola*), above. The male has a large head with a white patch. Like the other species, the female is brown with a white patch on her cheek.

Running along the shoreline are sanderlings (*Calidris alba*). These small, whitish birds feed on mole crabs, sand fleas, and worms as they move quickly up and down the intertidal zone.

The endangered piping plover (*Charadrius melodus*) can also be seen on a sandy beach. They are a slightly smaller bird. Their eggs are laid in open, sandy areas and are difficult to see. The Cape's beaches are popular recreational spots in the summer. The plover's population has been adversely affected by human activity and natural predators such as crows and coyotes. Hence there is a need to fence off nesting areas to protect these endangered birds.

Finally the great blue heron (*Ardea herodias*) is often seen walking slowly in the marshes. This large bird can be over four feet tall and has a grayish-blue plumage. It feeds on fish and other small animals in creeks and has been known to overwinter on the Cape during mild weather. When disturbed it emits a series of loud squawking sounds unique to the species.

GLOSSARY

ACIDIFICATION – the process in which atmospheric carbon dioxide reacts with water to form carbonic acid.

AIR BLADDER – a gas-filled structure found in rockweed which helps the alga float to the surface to maximize photosynthesis; also called pneumatocysts.

ALGIN – a gelatinous substance removed from some brown algae that has several commercial uses.

ALTERNATION OF GENERATIONS – two distinct stages (haploid and diploid) in the life cycle of an organism.

ANAEROBIC – an environment in which there is no oxygen.

ARISTOTLE'S LANTERN – a chewing structure found in sea urchins that enables them to graze on large algae.

ARTHROPOD – a bilaterally symmetrical animal with a segmented body.

BOOK GILLS – a structure in horseshoe crabs used for breathing and swimming.

BRYOZOAN – a microscopic colonial animal that is attached to a shell or rock.

BYSSAL THREADS – strong fibers used by mussels to attach to an object.

CALCIFICATION – the process of removing and depositing calcium carbonate or lime.

CARAPACE – the "shell" of a crab.

CARNIVORE – an animal that eats another animal.

CHELICERAE – a small pair of pincers which assist a horseshoe crab in feeding.

CHITIN – the substance that makes up the exoskeleton in crabs.

CHOANOCYTES (COLLAR CELLS) – specialized cells in sponges that assist in the movement of water through the animal.

CONCEPTACLE – the reproductive structures in rockweed that release the gametes into the water.

DETRITUS – decomposing organic material that provides a food source for animals in a marsh.

DIATOMS – a group of single-celled algae that are a major part of the phytoplankton.

DIPLOID – having both pairs of chromosomes in each cell.

ENDOSKELETON – an internal skeleton of an animal.

ENDOTOXIN – a poisonous substance found in the walls of some bacteria.

EPIDERMIS – the outside layer in a sponge that contains many pores.

EUTROPHICATION – the process of excess nutrients, such as nitrogen, which leads to a rapid growth of algae in a bay or estuary,

EXOSKELETON – an external skeleton of an animal.

FILTER-FEEDER – an animal that obtains its nutrition by straining food substances from water.

FROND – the leaf-like structure in algae.

GAMETOPHYTE – the life cycle generation in algae that contain the male (antheridia) and female (oogonia) reproductive structures.

GEMMULES – cyst-like reproductive cells in sponges that are resistant to environmental stress conditions.

HABITAT – the place where an organism obtains all of its requirements for life.

HAPLOID – having one of each pair of chromosomes in each cell.

HERBIVORES – animals that consume plants.

HERMOPHRODITIC – containing both male and female reproductive structures.

HOLDFAST – a root-like structure in seaweeds that attaches to a substrate.

INVERTEBRATE – an animal without a backbone.

JETTY – a structure made of rocks built at an angle along the coastline in order to block the movement of sand.

LEGUME – a member of the plant family Fabaceae in which the root nodules contain nitrogen-fixing bacteria.

MANTLE – a tissue surrounding the internal structure that is responsible for the formation of the shell.

MIDRIB – a supportive structure that runs along the center of rockweed.

MOLTING – the process of shedding an exoskeleton as an animal increases in size.

OSCULUM – an opening in sponges that leads to a central cavity.

PANNES – pools of water in a marsh that provide habitats for many small animals.

PERENNIAL – a plant that lives for more than two years.

PHOTOSYNTHESIS – the production of oxygen and sugars by plants using sunlight, water, carbon dioxide, and chlorophyll.

PINNATE LEAVES – a compound leaf with leaflets on each side of a central petiole or leaf stem.

PLANKTON – microscopic plants (phytoplankton) and animals (zooplankton) that drift in the water.

POLLINATION – the process in which the male pollen is transferred to the female stigma in a flower.

PREDATOR – an animal that feeds on another animal, its prey.

PRODUCER – an organism that makes its own food through the process of photosynthesis.

RADULA – a small, toothed structure in snails used for feeding.

REGENERATION – the re-growth of a structure or organ that is lost.

RHIZOME – an underground stem that can spread the growth of a plant.

SCAVENGER – an animal that feeds on dead animal material.

SIPHON – a tube-like structure in mollusks for the movement of water and food particles.

SPICULES – the needle-like structures that compose the body of a sponge.

SPOROPHYTE – the life cycle generation in algae that contains the spore-producing sporangia.

SUBSTRATE – a place or object on which an organism is attached or lives.

SYMBIOSIS – a relationship between two organisms in which one or both may benefit.

VASCULAR PLANTS – plants that contain conducting tissues for water and food.

WATER VASCULAR SYSTEM – a series of canals found in starfish for the movement of water.

WRACK LINE – the high tide mark characterized by the presence of eelgrass or seaweed.

ZONE – a division of the shoreline characterized by certain plants and animals.

ZYGOTE – the cell product of fertilization.

RECOMMENDED REFERENCES

Carson, Rachel. *The Edge of the Sea*, Houghton Mifflin Company, Boston. 1955.

Gosner, Kenneth L. *A Field Guide to the Atlantic Seashore*. Houghton Mifflin Company, Boston. 1978.

Meinkoth, Norman A. *The Audubon Society Field Guide to North American Seashore Creatures*. Alfred A. Knopf, New York. 1981.

Newton, Gilbert. *Seaweeds of Cape Cod Shores*. Cape Cod Museum of Natural History. West Barnstable Press. 2008.

Petry, Loren C. and Marcia G. Norman. *A Beachcomber's Botany*. The Chatham Conservation Foundation, Inc. Fifth Edition, Chatham, Massachusetts. 1982.

Waller, Geoffrey, Ed. *Sealife - A Complete Guide to the Marine Environment*. Smithsonian Institution Press, Washington, D.C. 1996.

Zim, Herbert S. and Lester Ingle. *Seashore Life*. St. Martin's Press. New York. 1989.

The Author

Gilbert Newton is a Cape Cod native who has been teaching environmental science at Sandwich High School and the Cape Cod Community College for many years. His classes include coastal ecology, botany, horticulture, coastal zone management, and environmental technology. He completed his graduate work in biology at Florida State University. Gil is one of the founders of the Barnstable Land Trust and a past president of the Thornton W. Burgess Society and of the Association to Preserve Cape Cod. He is the author of *Seaweeds of Cape Cod Shores* and *The Ecology of a Cape Cod Salt Marsh.*

The Photographer

Chris Dumas has lived and worked on Cape Cod for many years. He currently teaches earth and space science at Sandwich High School. Chris has been involved with outdoor education for most of his career. Photography has been an important part of Chris' life for the last decade and he has traveled around the country in search of interesting vistas. Chris has a graduate degree in Resource Conservation from the University of Montana and is a native of the St. Lawrence River Valley region of New York. His photography can also be seen in *The Ecology of a Cape Cod Salt Marsh.*

This book was designed and typeset by Nancy Viall Shoemaker of West Barnstable Press, West Barnstable, Massachusetts. The text font is Bookman Old Style, designed by Alexander Phemister in 1858, working from the font Caslon. It was constructed with straighter serifs, allowing it to keep its readability, even at small sizes. Photo credits were set in Frutiger, designed by Swiss typographer Adrian Frutiger (1928-). The font used for the chapter heads is Nueva. It was designed by Carol Twombly for Adobe in 1994. *Discovering the Cape Cod Shoreline* was printed on 70 lb. white opaque offset with a 12 pt. Kromekote cover.

Entire book, including cover, printed on recycled paper